Family Heirloom Book

"Grandma was Quite a Girl"

Tenth Printing

LIBRARY of CONGRESS Number: 78-64480

As Written by Grandmother
— With a little help from
"Thought Starters" and "Memory Jogs"

by Harry and Gloria McMahan

"Every family should write its own history!"

— This was the point made by Margaret Mead, the famous anthropologist and author, at the special three-day program, "Kin and Communities" sponsored by the Smithsonian Institution.

This special book was inspired by the idea. Why can't every family be encouraged to write their own history?

"Families make history — of themselves," the Smithsonian meeting underlined.

So here are the "thought starters" and "memory jogs" to get Grandmother to go back in her memory and write down that history, along with her own experiences. (There's another book for Grandpa, too.)

This, then, becomes a "family heirloom" for the children and the grandchildren and the children of generations to come.

So, Grandmother, it's all yours! Tell us all about it!

McMahan
Box 1537
Escondido, Calif. 92025

Dedicated to...

Erma Sibert McMahan, who in her 78 years saw a new century in and brought into this world four strapping sons to carry on her dreams, her ideals and her principles of life. The things she believed in live on.

INDEX

What is a Grandmother?

A grandmother is a little girl who suddenly shows up one day with a touch of gray in her hair.

Better than anything, she has a way of understanding little boys. Especially men who are grown-up little boys.

Something about a grandmother is always making you hungry. Maybe it's the apple pies baking and the chicken frying and the cookies in the oven. But grandma always has the nicest smelling house in all our memories.

Long before band-aids were invented, she was the best person to take care of scraped knees and scratched elbows and banged heads. If they could put her kind of love and medicine in a bottle, God could have opened a drug store. It was something in the way she touched you and the way her soft voice wrapped a bandage around your heart.

Grandmother was an expert on mischief, too. Especially when you had been into it. When she looked right into your eyes it was pretty hard to fool her about what really happened. Really.

And it was when you were almost too big to sit in her lap that you began to learn that she was a very special person to talk to. Sometimes, she would give you the right answers without ever saying a word. She had a way of listening that made the problems melt down to size.

How did a little girl ever grow up to be so smart? Maybe it came with the gray hair. Maybe it came suddenly with being a grandmother.

Anyway, I'm glad it came and I'm glad I became *me* . . . a special *me* . . . because of *her* . . .

H.W.M.

Family Photos

My Favorite

Photo

Today is ______________________________ and I am ______

years old.

I have lived a full, rich life and now I want to tell my family all about it.

To begin at the beginning, I was born in

______________________________, on ______________

in the year ______.

My parents officially named me ____________________, but I grew up with a few nicknames (some of which I'd rather not recall)!

GRANDMA'S PROVERBS:

Some of my neighborhood club have nothing to say. But you have to listen to them quite a long time before you realize it.

I Remember My Mother:

Mother was then ______ years old and My Father was ______.

As a child I remember the house we lived in:

____

____

____

____

____

____

____

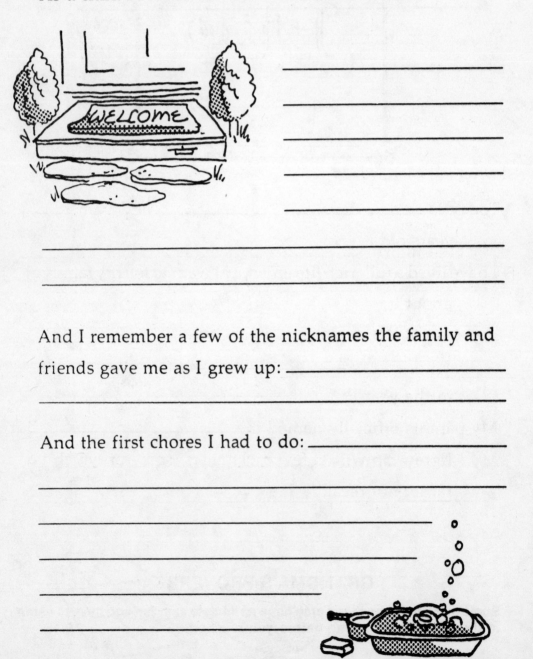

And I remember a few of the nicknames the family and friends gave me as I grew up: ______________________

____

And the first chores I had to do: ______________________

____

____

____

____

____

My Own First Memories:

My First — My *Very First* — Thing Remembered: ______

______

My First Day in School: ______

______

______

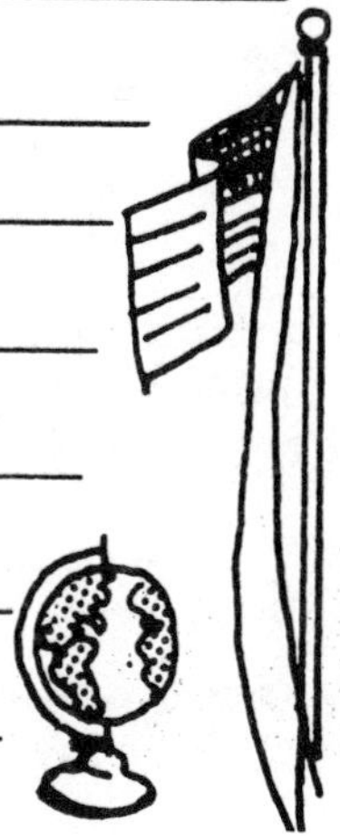

The Games We Played: ______

______

______

My First "Paddling" — and Why! ______

______

My First Injury: ______

______

______

______

My Nicest Neighbor: ______

______

My Favorite Teacher: ______

______

My First "Club": ______

______

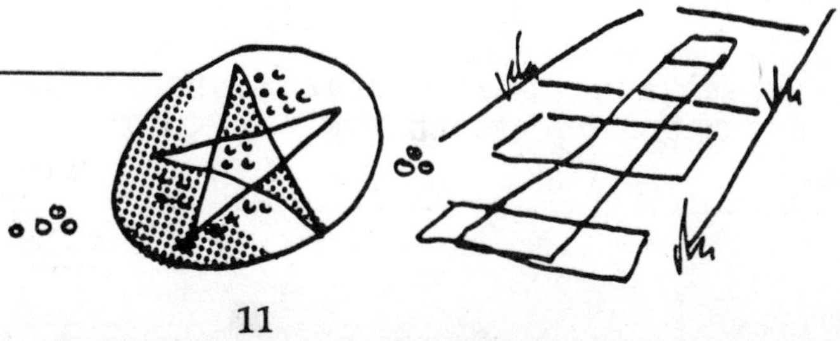

GRANDMA SAYINGS:

The Sea of Matrimony sure teaches you how to swim and keep your head above water.

A woman has the right to change her mind occasionally. Otherwise how would she keep it clean?

The web of our life is like a sweater we make. We set the pattern, learning as we knit. May the memories of the knitting help to keep us warm, just in case it ever unravels.

When I hear a girl say she "wants" a husband with good looks, brains, lots of money and a love only for her," I do my best to explain the penalties of bigamy.

Keep your eyes *wide open,* when courting you go —
After marriage, *half-shut* — for by now, you *know* . . .

The Electrical Age is wonderful.
Everything in the home today is controlled by switches — except the children . . .

Why does a woman with only two lips wind up with 14 lipsticks?

A bachelor is someone who doesn't believe in love at first sight because he's busy taking a second look.

page 13

1 – Blue
2 Rose
3
4
5
6
7
8

July 02, 1994

Favorites In My Memory:

My Favorite *Color:* ____________________

My Favorite *Flowers:* ____________________

My Favorite *Perfume:* ____________________

My Favorite *Day of the Year:* __________

My Favorite *Time of the Day:* __________

My Favorite *Musical Instrument:*

____

My Favorite *Poem:* ____________________

My Favorite *Melody:* ____________________

Up the Branches of Our Old Family Tree

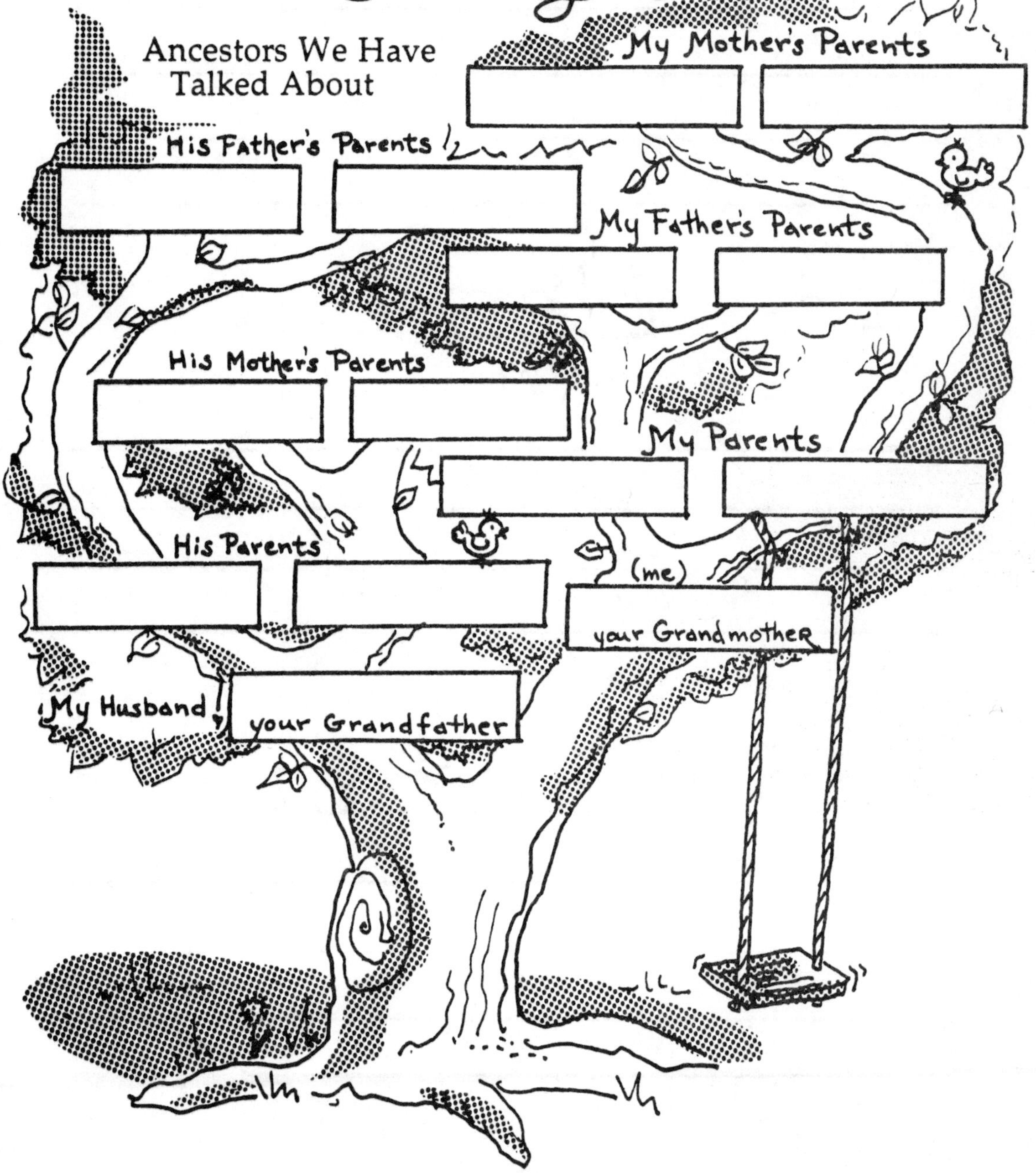

A Lot of Interesting People Went Before You!
And I hope you add some nice twigs after me!

My Favorite Aunt

(And Why!)

Uncle

(And Why!)

And Cousins:

GRANDMA SAID IT:

When they talk about conserving energy I have to remember a cousin who's been doing that for years . . .

My Father's Favorite Family Stories

My Mother's Favorite Family Stories

Happiness is a Man Called "Grandpa"

I met him______________________________

It was______wasn't______love at

first sight:

Our first date______________

His favorite nickname for me______________

We were engaged______________

And married__________on ____________________________

in__________at ____________________________________

And I wore ____________________________________

The Best Man____________________(it was *really* your grandfather!)

Our honeymoon: ______________________________________

____

The first place we lived ________________________________

____

Our first fight: _______________________________________

____

____

BEANS
CARROTS
EGG PLANT

MY BROTHERS & SISTERS

(Or why I wanted to be an Only Child!)

Their nicknames: ______________________________

____

____

Their Good & Bad Sides: ______________________________

____

____

____

Their Hobbies: ______________________________

____

____

Their Work: ______________________________

____

____

____

____

GRANDMA'S SCRAPBOOK:

Money is the root . . .
(of most family fights . . .!)

A Houseful of Relatives:

(And What I Think of Them!)

Their Names: (Now, see the numbers on the OPPOSITE PAGE — and see what I'd use to describe each:

____ ______________________________

____ ______________________________

____ ______________________________

____ ______________________________

____ ______________________________

____ ______________________________

____ ______________________________

____ ______________________________

YOU? Why I'd give *you* these numbers:

6, 12, 15, 19 (and maybe 25, too!)

GRANDMA OBSERVES:

A watched pot . . .

Tells you you're getting too fat . . .

Adjectives for Relatives:

1. crazy
2. funny
3. always laughing
4. truthful
5. courageous
6. loving
7. reliable
8. good
9. sourpuss
10. always crying
11. excitable
12. trustworthy
13. busybody
14. unreliable
15. sweet
16. honest
17. loyal
18. busy
19. dear
20. spooky
21. a kook!

Or I'd Say:

22. I wouldn't trust him with a rusty nickel ______
23. Goofy as a giraffe with a knot in his neck ______
24. Pure as the driven snow, but she drifted ______
25. Honest as the day is long — during an eclipse ______
26. He has a mind like a bear trap — he just hasn't caught anything yet ______

LISTEN TO GRANDMA:

It's all in the point of view: Some gardeners talk about the beautiful flowers they grow. Others can't talk about anything but the bugs that bother them.

My Own Grandparents:

— And how I remember them:

(Including a few things I've heard!)

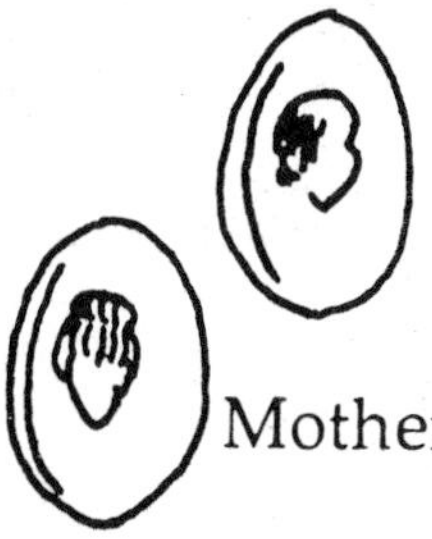

Mother's Folks:

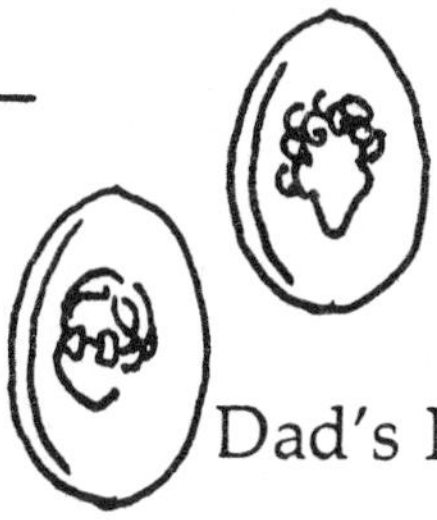

Dad's Folks:

GRANDMA'S GUESS:

I guess it's because we have such faults ourselves that we can take pleasure in hearing about the faults of others.

POPCORN

Good Times and Bad:

I was in a play ______________________________

____

I learned to dance ______________________________

____

I won a contest ______________________________

____

I got my first pet ______________________________

____

I had my first "date" ______________________________

____

I had the measles ______________________________

I had mumps ______________________________

I had chickenpox ______________________________

I had my tonsils out ______________________________

GRANDMOTHER SAYS:

**Talk's cheap —
until you get the bill from the phone company . . .**

4033

You: Who's Who

Outside of our immediate family, we have some famous — and wonderful — friends and relatives, like: ______________________________

GRANDMOTHER SAYS:

Let me be the mirror behind your candle —

Together we'll spread a lot more light . . .

As a Young Girl (& baby)

I was:

____ months old when I started to speak . . .

____ months old when I started to walk . . .

____ years old when I rode a tricycle . . .

____ years old when I learned to make my bed and clean my room . . .

____ years old when I learned to use a needle and thread . . .

____ years old when I thought I was old enough to wear a bra . . .

GRANDMA'S SAYINGS:

Why is it my parents thought they knew so much more than I did? — And now, my own children think so, too . . .

Growing Up

When I was this many years old:

____I got lost away, from home

____I first tried lipstick and rouge

____I smoked my first cigarette

____I had my first drink

____I had my first date

____I got a traffic ticket

____I got hauled into court

____I spent a night in jail

(Oh, yes — Grandma was quite a gal!)

GRANDMA'S NO-TOMFOOLERY:

Being a younger brother to triplets must be a tough job: Think of all the hand-me-downs you'd have to wear!

Growing Up . . .

I suppose you could describe me as:

____ Shy
____ brash
____ lean (skinny!)
____ pretty
____ romantic
____ intellectual
____ athletic (tomboy!)
____ adventurous
____ bold
____ timid
____ fat
____ *very* pretty!
____ *very* romantic
____ not smart — *shrewd*!
____ muscle-bound
____ poetic

LISTEN TO GRANDMA:

Every life is given a length of rope. We can use it to skip rope for skipping through the years, to bind ourselves to useful things, to make a hangman's knot, or to raise a flag on high.

The Dresses I Remember Most:

GRANDMA SAY-IT-FOR-TRUE:

The trouble with some of those fancy psychiatrists is that they never got enough lovin' when they were little boys.

GRANDMA'S SAYINGS:

Always remember: Today's caterpillar will be tomorrow's butterfly.

Want a warm, bright experience? —Keep the Christmas tree lights in your heart.

The more the world turns, the dizzier she gets.

Dr. Joyce Brothers says the average woman kisses 79 men before she gets married. I'm not sure I ever got my quota—can I start over now?

He who steals my purse steals credit cards.

Being bald-headed has its advantages, my friend Charlie says: "You can part your hair with a wash cloth."

As he gets older, I notice he dresses like a rainbow. Only the pot is on his front end.

Let's play "Kiss the Cook" again . . . hmmmmm, is something burning?

In my lifetime, "The Man in the Moon" became "A Man On the Moon". Both ideas are pretty romantic, if you ask me.

Love / Hate

✓ I Love — I Hate X

____ Getting up in the morning ____

____ Taking a cold bath ____

____ Talking to strangers ____

____ Having to buy a new hat ____

____ Going to the dentist ____

____ Buying a new car ____

____ Working with flowers ____

____ Watching television ____

____ Cooking Special Dishes ____

____ Cleaning House ____

____ Moving to a new home ____

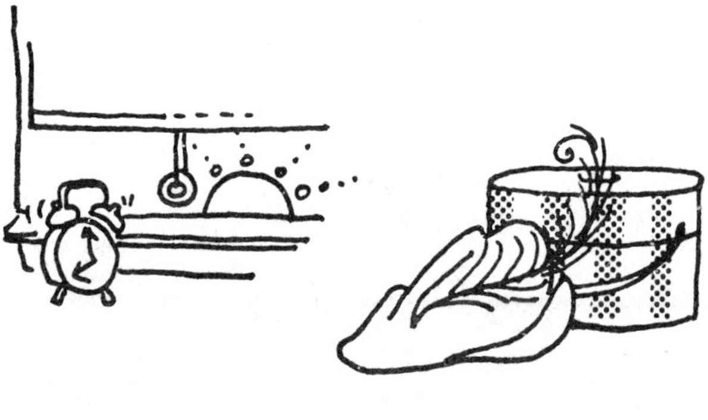

ASK GRANDMA:

"I always say: you have to keep doing a thing 'til you get it right . . ." Who said that? Zsa Zsa Gabor when she married her sixth husband . . .

Some Things I Have Broken:

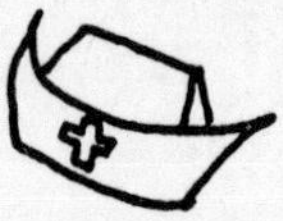

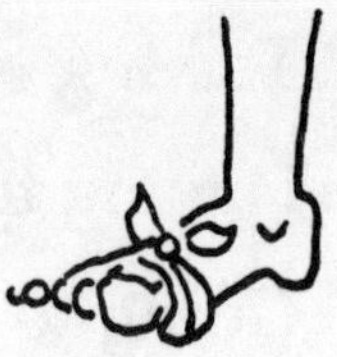

____ My arm:

____ My leg:

____ My collar-bone:

____ My big toe:

____ My heart:

____ A mirror (7 years' bad luck?)

____ A promise:

____ The 10 Commandments (Well, I fractured one once . . .)

(It's fun to Gossip . . .)

GRANDMA'S OBSERVATIONS:

**Every pillow knows:
Two heads are better than one . . .**

Things I Like to Collect

Friends, Of Course: ____________

And pretty china: ______________

And coins (oh, yes!) _______________

And recipes: _______________

And ____

____

____

GRANDMA'S PROVERBS:

A stitch in time . . .
(Is for sew-and sews . . .)

Things I Hated Doing

(As A Child)

Making my bed ____________________

Picking up my clothes ____________________

Putting my toys away ____________________

Keeping clean ____________________

Taking a bath ____________________

Wiping the dishes ____________________

Taking a nap ____________________

Writing "thank you" letters ____________________

Staying in on a rainy day ____________________

— See? — Things haven't changed so much for children today — and they've got tv!

GRANDMA NEVER FIBS:

Some men I know would rather take the wife out to Sunday dinner than have to wash the dirty dishes. That may be fair enough!

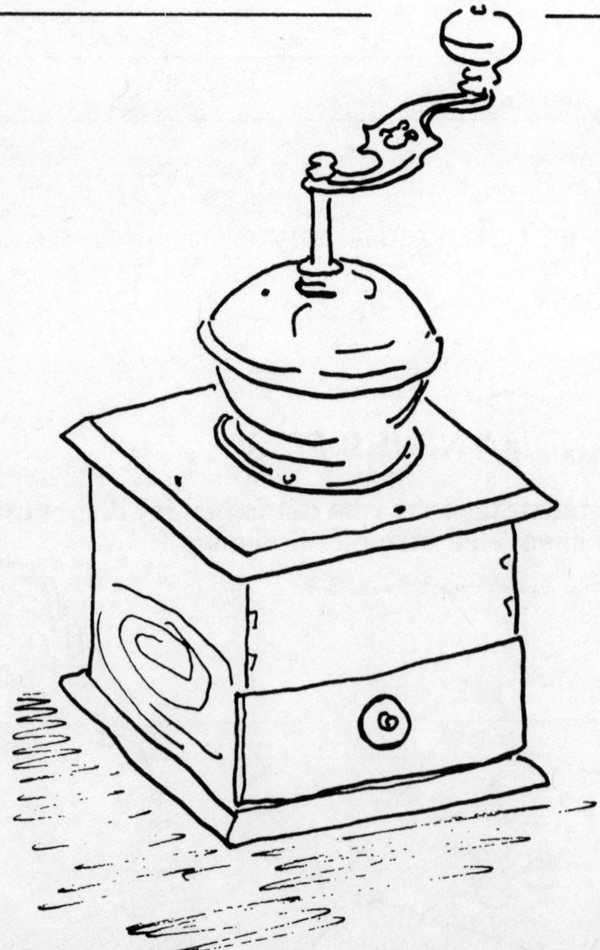

I Prefer

✓ // ✗

____ small town/big city ____

____ home cooking/restaurants ____

____ driving/just riding ____

____ early rising/late sleeping ____

____ doing my own hair/beauty parlor ____

____ earning money/spending it ____

____ apartment/house ____

____ one husband/two husbands ____

GRANDMA'S PROVERBS:

Honesty is the best policy . . .
— for losing friends . . . !

I DO BELIEVE/ I DON'T BELIEVE

✓ ✗

___ Alcohol is America's biggest problem ___

___ Taxes are too high for what you get ___

___ Most automobiles wear out too fast ___

___ Smoking is harmful to your health ___

___ Women's Lib isn't working like it should ___

GRANDMA'S SUGGESTION:

Come New Year's Day, write down 10 things you believe in . . .

Come Fourth of July, count whether your mind is still spry enough to change .

My Greatest Ambition:

As a Little Girl: ______________________________

____

In My Teens: ______________________________

____

____

____

Before I got carried away in Marriage: ______________

____

____

____

After I married: ______________________________

____

____

And Still: ______________________________

____

____

____

Family Photos

GRANDMOTHER SAYS:

**Why is it I hate thunder —
and adore lightning . . . ?**

When I Look Back — I Have to Laugh a Little

The silliest thing I ever did:

The second silliest thing I ever did:

The SMARTEST thing I ever did:

Pastimes in Past Times

Playing with dolls.

____

Playing house:

____

Helping make a cake:

____

Licking the ice cream paddle:

____

Popping corn:

____

Playing with boys:

____

Making daisy chains:

____

Pulling Taffy:

____

Slumber parties:

____

Toasting marshmallows:

____

Surprise parties:

____

Some of the First Loves of My Life:

Rag Doll ______________________________

Teddy Bear ______________________________

Rocking Horse ______________________________

China Doll ______________________________

Building blocks ______________________________

Cook Stove ______________________________

Doll Dishes ______________________________

A Cradle for my Doll ______________________________

Crossing my eyes! ______________________________

The Fir$t$

The first money I ever earned — *really* earned: ____________

____

____

____

The first paycheck job I ever held: ________________

____

____

____

The first time I bought something *"big"* with my own money:

____

____

____

____

GRANDMA'S AXIOMS:

A fool and his money
— are soon party-ed . . .

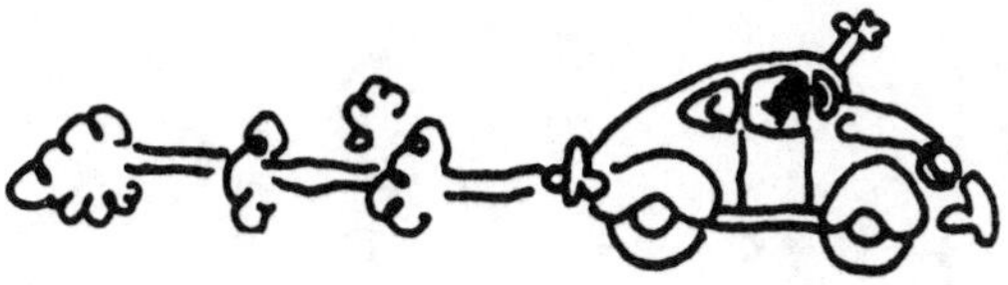

The first time I drove — the first car I remember: ______

______

______

______

The first time I paid the rent: ______

______

______

______

The most important purchase I ever made: ______

______

______

______

SAY IT WITH GRANDMA:

It's hard getting used to your first gray hair.
— But you have to accept it — until the day you dye . . .

"The Bests"

The Best Vacation I ever had, growing up!:

The Best Year I enjoyed in school:

The Best car we ever owned:

My first "Best Sweetheart" — till I was 10:

My next "Best Sweetheart" — till I was 20:

My best "Best Sweetheart" since:

SAY IT WITH GRANDMA:

The cosmetics business seems to be born of strange parents: Mother Nature & Father Time.

— If only they'd quit fighting you . . .

My Favorite

My favorite saying always has been: ______________________

____

My favorite person — outside the family:

____

My favorite pet of my lifetime: __________

____

And some other pets I well remember:

____

____

My favorite hobby: ______________________________

____

____

____

GRANDMA'S DICTIONARY:

ASTROLOGY: A very convenient way to blame something else for any bad luck that you happen to have . . .

Family Photos

Why I.... Never Had Enough CLOSETS

In my lifetime I estimate I have owned:

___ pair of hose

___ pair of panties

___ pair of shoes

___ pair of gloves

___ slips

___ bras

___ dresses

And I've eaten, in my lifetime, maybe:

___ dozen eggs

___ gallons of milk

___ slices of bread

___ pieces of pie

___ cups of coffee

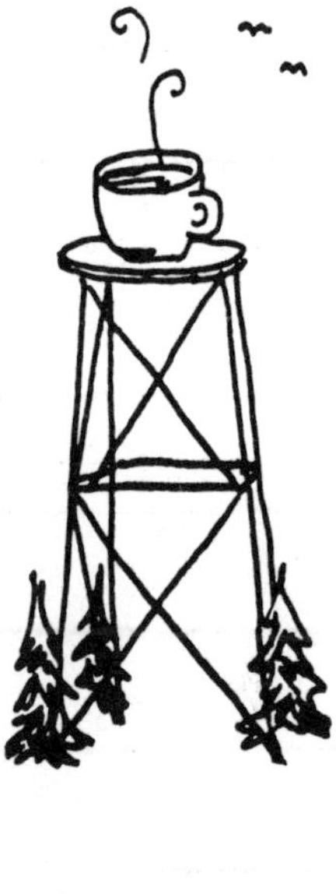

(— I guess I was pretty hungry!)

SAY IT WITH GRANDMA:

Caffein is a stimulant. That's why a little stimulating gossip goes well when the girls get together for morning coffee.

My Helpful Household Hints (JUST CALL ME "Heloise!")

Some Funny Things:

The funniest joke anyone ever played on me:

The funniest joke I ever played on someone else:

— And my most embarrassing moment:

The funniest thing that happened on my honeymoon:

The funniest thing that happened at school:

The funniest thing that ever happened at home:

GRANDMA NEVER FIBS:

Little tears often are cured just with a big hug.

Traveling

The first trip I remember:

The first train ride I remember:

The first airplane trip I remember:

My favorite city when I was young:

My favorite hotel:

Some cities I would still like to visit:

GRANDMA'S PROVERBS

A rolling stone gathers no moss . . . but you might notice it manages to get a very handsome polish . . .

The U.S.A.

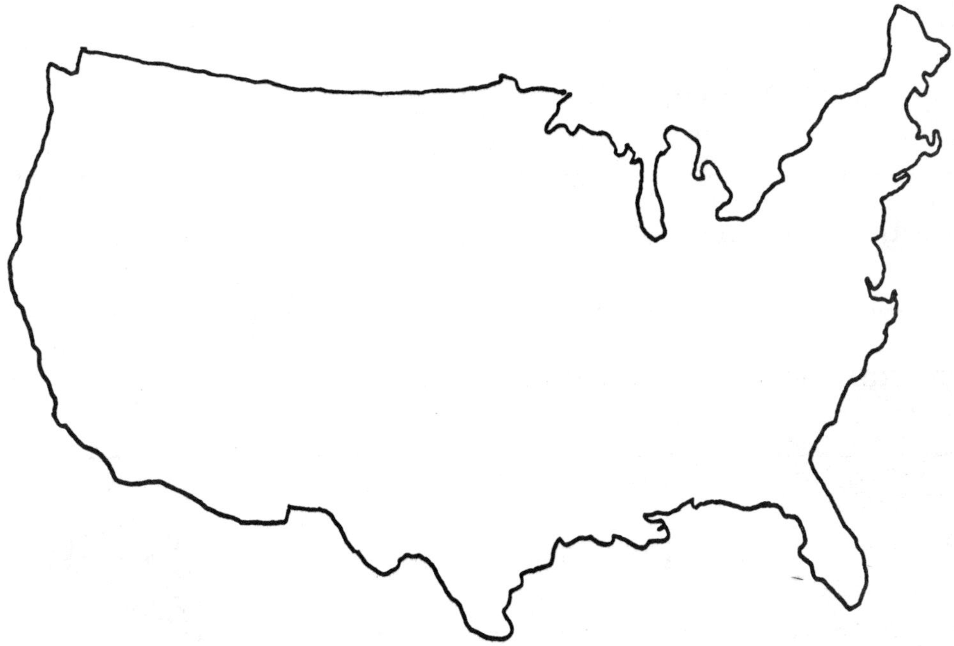

Cities I Have Visited

GRANDMA'S SUNDAY WISDOM:

Nothing combines joy and sadness together like packing a bag.

The "-est" Things

The sickest I ever got:

____

The maddest I ever got:

____

The tiredest I ever got:

____

The most jealous I ever got:

____

The smartest trick I ever pulled:

____

The biggest mistake I made in my life:

____

The luckiest I ever was:

____

The proudest I ever was:

____

GRANDMA THINK-ABOUT-ITS:

The quickest way to a man's heart may be through his stomach, but then why does he get around to saying he has to go on a diet?

I Guess I've Known a Few "Odd Balls"

The Craziest Kid I had as a Playmate:

The Nuttiest Girl in School:

The Worst Teacher I ever knew:

The Meanest Man in Town:

The Funniest Joker I ever Met:

The Kookiest Gal I ever Met:

The Most Memorable Person I ever Met:

— And the One Person Who Most Influenced My Life:

ASK GRANDMA:

Men find it hard to forget when they didn't have to hire domestic help — they married it.

The Happiest Christmas That I... Remember:

As a Child:

As a Young Girl:

In My Teens:

After I Married:

After my Children Were Born:

— But, there was *ONE* Christmas I'd Rather Forget:

Happy Holidays

My most exciting Valentine's Day:

My noisiest Fourth of July:

My most romantic New Year's Eve:

My gladdest Christmas season:

My happiest Thanksgiving:

My craziest Halloween:

GRANDMA SAY-IT-FOR-TRUE:

Why do trees always leave in the fall . . . just when you wish they'd stay?

Everything Happens to Me:

(Well, some of these Things, at Least. . .)

I was in an accident: ______________________________

____

I was in an earthquake: ____________________________

____

I was in a fire: _________________________________

____

I was in a tornado: _______________________________

____

I was in a fight: _________________________________

____

I was robbed: ___________________________________

____

I was caught naked: ____________

____

But, ONE TIME, I was a heroine:

____

____

GRANDMA'S ADVICE:

The worst thing about a cold is listening to a lot of advice from your friends.

More First Times

– The First Time I ever gambled —

–The First Time I ever went fishing—(and caught a fish *this* big!)

– The First Time I was angry enough to hit someone —

– The First Time I sold something —

– The First Time I fell in love —

My "Auto" Biography

(Family Cars I Remember Well)

Ford
Apperson
Chevy
Buick
VW
Toyota
Model T
Opel
Overland
Oldsmobile
Rolls-Royce
Dodge
Imperial
Jeep
Edsel

Cougar
Bobcat
Hornet
Mustang
Pinto
Maverick
Cricket
T-Bird
Colt
Impala
Road Runner
Ram
Subaru
Packard
Citroën

Pontiac
Volvo
Fiat
Renault
Simca
Mitchell
Marmon
Lafayette
Nash
Hudson
Jaguar
DeSoto
Chrysler
Pierce-Arrow

And My Own First "Wheels":

Scooter ______

Roller Skates ______

Bicycle ______

Red wagon ______

Skate Board ______

Tricycle ______

Men Are Wonderful—Except...

Except . . .

— when they tell you how to drive . . .

— when they tell you how to hold a hammer . . .

— when they try to explain where they've been . . .

— when they have to buy a new suit . . .

— when they try to judge a likely son-in-law

I think the 3 most interesting men in history were:

Adam ____

Noah____

Solomon ____

King Henry VIII ____

Napoleon ____

George Washington ____

Valentino ____

____

Cary Grant ____

Clark Gable ____

Wm. Holden ____

Bing Crosby ____

Dean Martin ____

Robert Redford ____

Jack Kennedy ____

____

More Likes & Dislikes

My favorite singer:

___

My favorite newspaper:

___

My favorite TV star:

___

The best movie I ever saw:

___

My favorite movie star:

___

My favorite romantic novel:

___

The *worst* movie star of all:

___

GRANDMA'S OWN PROVERBS:

As you sew . . .
so shall you rip . . .

Family Recipe Favorites

GRANDMA SAID IT:

Love is food for the soul . . .

And certain "special foods" in the family can become the soul of love . . .

More About Food and Cooking . . .

My favorite food as a child: ____________

____

My favorite as a girl: ____________

____

My life-time favorite: ____________

____

My favorite restaurant: ____________

____

One of the best meals I ever ate — anywhere:

____

The first food I learned to cook myself: ____________

____

My favorite recipe to pass along: ____________

____

GRANDMA'S PROVERBS:

Man does not live by bread alone — I know . . . and I've cooked more than 38,000 meals to prove it . . . !

The Ten Foods I Like or Dislike

__✓__ YES __X__ NO

______ artichoke ______

______ apple pie ______

______ tamales ______

______ kidney pie ______

______ eggs ______

______ liver ______

______ boiled cabbage ______

______ ice cream ______

______ spinach ______

______ watermelon ______

______ steak ______

______ broccoli ______

______ mush ______

______ squash ______

______ pigsfeet ______

______ snails ______

______ lettuce ______

GRANDMA THINK-ABOUT-ITS:

Which came first, the chicken or the egg? Depends on whether you're cookin' chicken pot-pie or scrambled eggs.

Things to Come: and I'd Like to Live Long Enough to See!

1. A cure for cancer

2. Safer cars

3. Abolition of poverty

4. Peace (more than $2/3$rds of my years there has been a War on — somewhere!)

5.

6.

7.

8.

GRANDMA'S PROVERBS:

Overeating is the lot of too many people. It is a destiny that ends our shapes . . . and shapes our ends . . .

My OWN Opinions:

Peace will never come until: ______________________________

____

The trouble with airplanes: ______________________________

____

Swimming in the nude: ______________________________

____

How to solve the world's overpopulation problems:

____

____

Woman was never intended to have only *one* man:

____

____

GRANDMA SAID IT:

Brevity is, they say, the soul of wit. Maybe that's why swim suit styles often seem kind of funny to me.

Babies! Babies! Babies

I keep thinking of the names I would have named the "more babies" if I had had all I ever wanted: ____________________

____

Now, for *girls*, I'd liked to have been "Mother" to such sweet names as:

____

____

And, for boys, I guess I would have changed diapers and put up with their foolishness if I'd given them names like:

____

____

— Yes, we might have been a *large family*!

THE WORD FROM GRANDMA:
Some cows give milk. From other cows you have to take it.

I Wish, I Wish, I Wish—

I Wish I Had:

____ Studied other languages, especially ________________________

____ Kept my Indian penny collection

____ Kept my first doll

____ Kept a real diary, all the years of my life

____ Kept more pictures of the people and places I knew

____ Asked my Mother and Father more questions about *their* lives

____ And I wish I could talk to *one* particular person ________________________

. . . just *one* more time . . .

GRANDMA'S SUNDAY WISDOM:

She finally decided there wasn't any new diet worth going on. She's what I'd call a poor loser.

GRANDMA'S SAYINGS:

Absence makes the heart grow fonder. Presents make it grow fonder still.

Why is it fat people have fat dogs?

I like that doctor who says, "Walking is your best exercise!" At least you don't need a prescription for it . . .

An old man realizes it takes money to make the mare go. Especially if he's horsing around.

Why is it, when it's my turn to have the car, the gas tank is almost empty?

Isn't it odd: millions of mothers and thousands of doctors can't get kids to eat carrots and spinach. But you know who can? —Bugs Bunny and Popeye the Sailor Man!

He's what you call a real sportsman. He's always shooting rabbits, shooting dice or he's down at the pool hall shooting the breeze.

Some people try to make life a one-way street — forgetting that, that way, there's no one ever coming to meet you . . .

My Favorite Games + Sports

(Marked: "1-2-3" as I like 'em)

___ Tennis

___ Swimming

___ Horseback Riding

___ Football

___ Baseball

___ Horse shoes

___ Horse Racing (& Betting!)

___ Fishing

___ Hunting

___ Tiddle-de-Winks

___ Ping-Pong

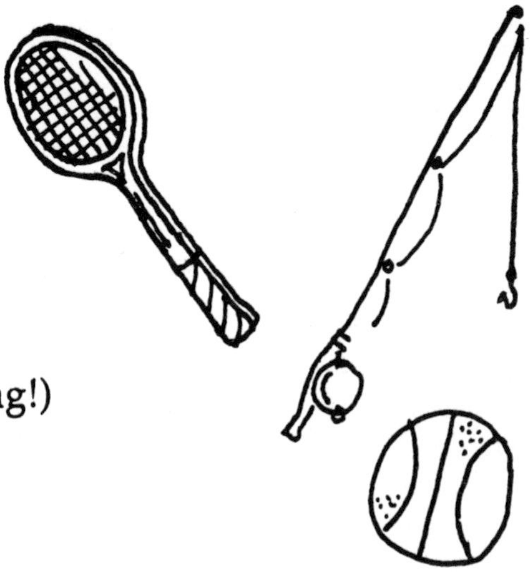

— And the nearest I ever came to being a Sport Champ —

____

____

____

GRANDMA REFLECTS:

Something baking in the oven . . .
Tells someone someone's loving' . . .

IF—

If I had it all to do over, I'd like to:

— Be born a boy, because: ____________________

____

____

— Be born in a family with ____ brothers and ____ sisters.

— Be born in a small town like ____________________

— With a new name of my own, like ________________

— And grow up to have a special work: ______________

____

____

— And get married ____ times

— And have ____ children!

— Or, maybe, really . . .

I wouldn't change a thing!

GRANDMA'S ADVICE:

Discipline needs to get to the bottom of the trouble . . . before it gets to the bottom.

In The Driver's Seat:

I can drive:

A car ____

A tractor ____

A hard bargain ____

A 10-penny nail ____

A pair of mules ____

A camel ____

A dog-sled team ____

A racing car ____

A horse to water ____

(But I can't make him drink)

And I can:

Pick a lock ____ Put up preserves____

Figure out puzzles ____

Work over half the cross-word puzzle ____

Barbecue a steak ____ Mow the grass____

Figure out the horse races ____

Guess people's ages ____

Milk a cow ____ Dance a jig____

And make dinner in 10 minutes when I have to ____

GRANDMA NEVER FIBS:

Did you ever notice: When a man's argument is weaker, his voice gets stronger? Maybe that's how he thinks he makes a *sound argument*.

IT WAS A GREAT CENTURY TO LIVE IN

The 20th Century Had Both Good and Bad,

But the Great Things Were Really Great:

Let me tell you what I know about the

Depression Years — the 'Thirties —

____

____

____

The Worst Year, I Guess, Was When I:

____

My Favorite Years Were:

____

And the War Years — the 'Forties:

____

____

____

____

The fast-moving 'Sixties & 'Seventies:

____

____

I Lived In a World of New Inventions

(And What I Liked About Each)

Radio —

Air Travel —

Vitamins —

Plastics —

Air-Conditioning —

Frozen Foods —

Space Travel —

GRANDMA'S PROVERBS:

Money is the root of all evil.
And the lack of it is nothing to root for, either.

MORE

Inventions

Television —

Computers —

Slacks —

Movies That Talked —

Improved Cars —

"The Pill" —

GRANDMA SAY-IT-FOR-TRUE:

I know a man who remembers how little things cost when he was young. And then I have to remind him: how little he earned . . .

Politics:

The first President I voted for:

____

The political office I believe I could have handled — better than a man!: ______________________________

____

What politicians today need most: ______________________________

____

____

The most famous politician I ever met:

____

The first time I voted was:

____

____

The political party I believe in: ______________________________

____

GRANDMA'S CAUTIONS:

Politics makes strange bedfellows —
And you'd better look and see exactly what they're trying to hide under that bed . . .

My Ten Best Friends Before I Was 10:

1

2

3

4

5

6

7

8

9

10

My Ten Best Friends - As a Young Lady

1

2

3

4

5

6

7

8

9

10

My Ten Best Friends - For Life

1. ______________________________

____

2. ______________________________

____

3. ______________________________

____

4. ______________________________

____

5. ______________________________

____

6. ______________________________

____

7. ______________________________

____

8. ______________________________

____

9. ______________________________

____

10. ______________________________

. . . more Recipes

GRANDMA OBSERVES:

A watched pot . . .
Tells you you're getting too fat . . .

Am I a... "Liberated Woman?"

What I think about:

The Right to Vote —

____

Equal Job, Equal Pay —

____

Youth and the "New Morals" —

____

Abortion —

____

"Unisex" —

____

Psychiatrists — ♀♂

____

Today's Increasing Divorce Rate
(3 Times what it was when I was a girl!)

____

— And I still like for a Man to Open the Door for Me . . .

____

THE WORD FROM GRANDMA:

Lincoln may have freed the slaves, but I'd rather celebrate the birthday of the man who invented the automatic washing machine.

Who's Superstitious?

Of course, I'm not superstitious, but I think it wise to use good caution when:

a. I walk under a ladder: ____

b. A black cat crosses my path: ____

c. On Friday, the 13th: ____

d. When I break a mirror: ____

e. When I get the turkey's wishbone: ____

f. After being married to the same man for 13 years! ____

And, there's a *ghost story* I believe in ______________

(I should — I lived through it!) ______________

____

____

____

____

____

____

____

GRANDMA'S PROVERBS:

A bird in the hand . . .
(Is very bad table manners . . .)

54

Good Deeds

The 3 nicest good deeds others have done for me:

And the 3 nicest I have tried to do for others:

GRANDMA'S own AXIOMS:

You can catch more flies with honey. . .
— But are you sure it was flies that you wanted to catch . . . ?

What I Think About People in general:

Rich people: ______________________

____

Poor People: ______________________

____

People Who Gossip: ______________________

____

Fat People: ______________________

____

Skinny People: ______________________

____

People Who Talk Too Much: ______________________

____

People Too Dumb: ______________________

____

People Too Book Smart: ______________________

____

GRANDMA OPINES:

They say travel broadens you —
I'm sure it's those rich foreign desserts . . .

How "Grandmothers" are Different from "Mothers":

GRANDMA'S NO-TOMFOOLERY:

Different people get boiling mad at different temperatures. And it takes a little time in marriage to "read" the thermometer on your husband.

"HELLO"
MAMA

If I Were to Give My Best Advice to My Grandchildren

Grandma's Final Say:

It was a good month in the magazines: I collected 14 new recipes, 14 of which I'll probably never get around to using.

Cordell Hull said it: Never insult an alligator until after you have crossed the river.

Man's Law: The bigger the closet, the more the junk.

Men who wear shirts as bright as the rainbow generally have pots at the end.

They say garlic is good to help prevent colds. Well, it certainly prevents any infectious kissing . . .

Christmas toys! Ol' Dad's deluded
He thought the batteries included . . .

I'd like to meet a woman who considers her young son a safe driver.

In any bank, it's safe to bet
The "other line" moves faster, yet . . .

My "Next-to-Last" Last Will & Testament:

More important than money are some of the things I give to my Children — and my Children's Children:

I give LOVE (a life-time full of it — love that you give generously and you earn full measure of, in return)

I give HAPPY MEMORIES (for these are the woven fabrics of our lives)

I give GOOD LUCK (and always the eager hope for a lottery ticket that wins!)

And LONG LIFE and an APPRECIATION for it (even as I have found it ever so wonderful) —

(And may you remember me well . . .)